TRANSFORMED

This book belongs to

. . . .

CONTENTS

BRAND NEW **IN HIM**

We can trust God's plan for us

Draw the angry face of Paul

Before

Draw the happy face of Paul after he met Jesus

After

Find out more about Paul, who used to be called Saul, in Acts 9:1–22

WHAT DO YOU THINK?

- Why was Paul going to Damascus?

- What happened to Paul on his way to Damascus?

- Who or what made Paul different?

- What was God's plans for Paul's future life?

PRAY

- Thank God that He has a great plan for your future

- Tell God that you trust His plan for you and your family

ACTS 9:1–22

FOREVER BLESSED BY HIM

God has chosen to bless us

ZACCHAEUS MAZE
Help Zacchaeus get to the tree so he can see Jesus

Find out more about
Zacchaeus in Luke 19:1–9

WHAT DO YOU THINK?

- How do you feel when someone gives you something special?

- Jesus has chosen you to be His special friend! Do you want to say 'yes' to Jesus? *(You could use the prayer at the end of Week Seven)*

PRAY

- Thank God that He has chosen you to be His friend forever

- Thank Jesus for His kindness and love towards you

- Ask Jesus to help you show kindness and love to others (name some people you could be kind to)

LUKE 19:1–9

PRAY TO KNOW
HIM BETTER

> ## 'Be still, and know that I am God'
> Psalm 46:10

Draw a circle around the pictures that show a
quiet place to spend time with Jesus

Find out more about Mary of Bethany in Luke 10:38–42

WHAT DO YOU THINK?

- Say this rhyme and do the actions:

   Here is busy Martha *(hold up one thumb)*
   Working all the day *(wiggle thumb around)*
   Too busy to listen to Jesus
   Too busy to hear what He says
   Here is listening Mary *(hold up other thumb)*
   Listening all the day *(keep thumb still)*
   Wanting to listen to Jesus
   Wanting to hear what He says

- Think about your own response to Jesus

   Will I be too busy to hear what Jesus says?
   Or will I listen to Him?
   Which will I do today?

PRAY

- Tell God how much you love Him

- Tell God what you have done wrong and say sorry

- Think of good things and people in your life and say thank You to God

- Pray for something you need help with

- Listen to God telling you how much He loves you

LUKE 10:38–42

7

ALIVE FOR **HIS PURPOSE**

God makes us new and gives us good things to do

Based on Ephesians 2:10

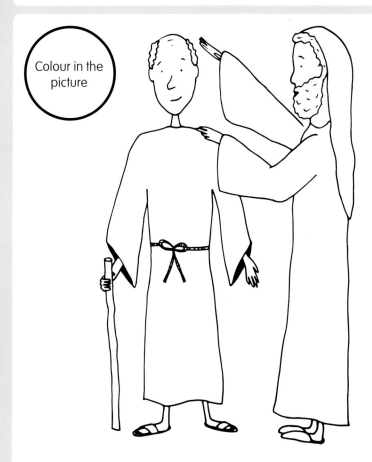

Colour in the picture

Which person is Jesus? Who is the other person?

Find out more about the men who were healed from leprosy in Luke 17:11–19

WHAT DO YOU THINK?

- Read Psalm 139:14 together: *'I praise you because you made me in such a wonderful way. I know how amazing that was!'* (Easy-to-Read Version)

- Create a **'thankful bag'** this week. Use a large paper bag and decorate the outside. Add the label 'My Thankful Bag'. Throughout the week, add items to the bag that you are thankful for; it could be a toy, pictures of your family, or a rock to represent God's creation. At the end of the week, have a thankful party to thank God for all of His many blessings.

PRAY

- Thank God that He has wonderfully made us, each of us, just as He planned us to be

- Thank God for the many wonderful things He does in your life each day

- Thank God that He wants to do wonderful things in your life **every** day!

LUKE 17:11–19

BELONG TO **HIS FAMILY**

If we love Jesus, we are part of God's family

Draw your family here

WHAT DO YOU THINK?

- Who do you know who is in God's family?
  (Mention yourself, people in the church, other people you know who love and follow Jesus)

- Talk about what we do as part of God's family (such as singing, playing, praying, church or Sunday school)

PRAY

- Thank God for each person in your family

- Thank God for the church family that you're part of

- Take time to listen to God – He wants you to know that He loves you being part of His family

ACTS 2:42–47

GIFTED TO SERVE HIM

God has made us special, so that we can show His love to others

Draw a circle around the pictures that show ways to serve

WHAT DO YOU THINK?

- What's special about you? What can you do well?

- How can you use this to help or show kindness to someone else?

- Make a plan to help others this week

PRAY

- Thank God for making you special

- Ask God to tell you who you could help this week.

  Write the person's name here:

  ....

- Ask God to show you how to help this person

MATTHEW
25:14–23

PRAY TO **KNOW HIM MORE**

With God's power working in us, he can do much, much more than anything we can ask or think of

Based on Ephesians 3:20

When Bartimaeus was blind, he couldn't see anything at all, not even colours. But when he could see, it was amazing!

Colour in the picture to show all the colours Bartimaeus could see after Jesus healed him

WHAT DO YOU THINK?

- Close your eyes to see what it is like not to be able to see. Open them again. What colours can you see?

- Bartimaeus called out Jesus' name because he knew Jesus could help him. When Bartimaeus met Jesus he wanted to know Jesus better.

- Would you like to know Jesus better? How about telling Jesus your answer?

PRAY

- If you would like to know Jesus better, say this prayer:

'Dear Jesus,
I know I do wrong things. I am really sorry.
Please wash them away and make me clean.
Jesus, I know You are God's Son and that
You died for me. Come live in my heart and
be my Friend forever. Amen.'

MARK
10:46–52

A NOTE FOR PARENTS

We hope that you and your child find this book helpful over the next seven weeks, as you go on the Transformed Life journey. To help your child understand the words of Paul in Ephesians, each session has been illustrated with a character or story from the Bible.

We would like to encourage you to support your child with this material. Younger children may need help with finding the passages in the Bible, reading the text and completing the creative elements.

May you find this time with your child a real blessing, as you seek to guide their understanding of what a transformed life looks like.

Copyright © 2015 Kingsgate
Published 2015 by CWR, Waverley Abbey House, Waverley Lane, Farnham, Surrey GU9 8EP, UK.
CWR is a Registered Charity – Number 294387 and a Limited Company registered in England – Registration Number 1990308.
The right of KingsGate to be identified as the author of this work has been asserted by them in accordance with the Copyright, Designs and Patents Act 1988; sections 77 and 78.
All rights reserved. No part of this publication may be reproduced, stored in a retrieval system, or transmitted, in any form or by any means, electronic, mechanical, photocopying, recording or otherwise, without the prior permission in writing of CWR.
For a list of National Distributors visit www.cwr.org.uk/distributors
Unless otherwise indicated, all Scripture references are from the Holy Bible, New International Version Anglicised (NIV) Copyright © 1979, 1984, 2011 by Biblica (formerly International Bible Society). Used by permission of Hodder & Stoughton Publishers, an Hachette UK company. All rights reserved. 'NIV' is a registered trademark of Biblica (formerly International Bible Society). UK trademark number 1448790. Other Scripture quotations are marked: Easy to Read Version, Copyright © 2006 by World Bible Translation Center.
Concept development, editing, design and production by KingsGate and CWR
Cover image: CWR and OneDollarPhotoClub/ Jag_cz
Printed in the UK by Linney Group
ISBN: 978-1-78259-442-0